CW00672684

WHERE'S NIGEL?

100% UNAUTHORISED ☒

Find Farage before his dreams
of power become reality!

HarperCollinsPublishers

HarperCollins*Publishers*
I London Bridge Street
London SEI 9GF

www.harpercollins.co.uk

First published by HarperCollins*Publishers* 2015

IO 9 8 7 6 5 4 3 2 I

Text © HarperCollins*Publishers* 2015

Illustrations © Jorge Santillan 2015

Jorge Santillan asserts his moral right to be identified as the
illustrator of this work

A catalogue record of this book is available from the British Library

ISBN 978-0-00-814212-4

Printed and bound in Italy by L.E.G.O. S.p.A.

All rights reserved. No part of this publication may be reproduced, stored in
a retrieval system, or transmitted, in any form or by any means, electronic,
mechanical, photocopying, recording or otherwise, without the prior written
permission of the publishers.

MIX
Paper from
responsible sources
FSC™ C007454

FSC™ is a non-profit international organisation established to promote the
responsible management of the world's forests. Products carrying the FSC
label are independently certified to assure consumers that they come from
forests that are managed to meet the social, economic and ecological needs
of present and future generations, and other controlled sources.

Find out more about HarperCollins and the environment at
www.harpercollins.co.uk/green

INTRODUCTION

Nigel Farage – the most divisive character in UK politics since Russell Brand – is splitting his time equally between Twitter and an odyssey across Britain and beyond, in a bid to achieve his party's dream of actually winning a seat in the General Election.

Your mission, should you choose to accept it (and given that you've read this far you might as well), is to locate Nigel in every picture. Like so many other Ukippers (are you *sure* about your next-door neighbours?), he's hiding in plain sight.

Look for him holding court in the European Parliament, taking in the court at Wimbledon and, ahem, being caught rubbing shoulders with Romanian immigrants, breast-feeding mothers and the inhabitants of an NHS waiting room. Keep your eyes peeled for him as he indulges in the national sport – pheasant shooting – and at Heathrow Airport (or the Migrant Interchange, as it's known at UKIP HQ).

And for the eagle-eyed among you, have a butcher's for some of Nigel's friends, colleagues and rivals among the crowd. The faces to look out for will be detailed on each picture, but you can safely assume the likes of Boris Johnson, David Cameron, Ed Miliband and Andy Murray's mum will be there too.

Happy hunting!

DOWNING STREET DREAM

Every man has a dream, and when Nigel isn't suffering from Romanian apocalypse nightmares, he loves to imagine himself leading the country. But it's a dream others have too. Can you spot Ed Miliband in there? And people's PM Russell Brand? Red-blooded lads the pair of 'em, though perhaps for different reasons ...

AT HEATHROW

It takes guts and hard work to conquer America. For every bout of Beatlemania there's a Cheryl coming home Cowelled and humiliated. After Boris Johnson's American tour, Nigel follows suit, though he's understandably nervous – after all, he'll be the migrant stateside, and isn't this where all those jihadi brides hitch a lift to Syria? Now, where is Nigel hiding? Fox News are desperate for an interview ...

AT LEICESTER SQUARE

UKIP's was always a story for the big screen, and Nigel is nothing if not leading-man material. He's ordered the red carpet in a colour more befitting of a purple revolution, of course, and Sarah Palin has invited him for a post-premiere Tea Party. Can you spot her too?

ON THE M4

Romania's chief export is telecoms equipment, not workers desperate to take our jobs, but don't let mere facts spoil Nigel's Romanian invasion for you. Nigel's fever dream has swamped the M4, but where is the man himself, sleepwalking through his own seventh circle of hell?
And can you spot Labour's pink-or-maybe-magenta-and-proud van?

AT THE SEASIDE

The last time Nigel had his top off at the beach and someone said, 'Pasty,' they got a gobful of Cornwall's finest. Thankfully, Nigel's keeping his clothes on here, but he fully intends to fight them on the beaches, with his Ukippers in tow. Can you find Nigel? If only to tell him it isn't 1940?

IN HOSPITAL

Nigel takes on healthcare – a political hot potato – after having a funny turn, which wasn't potato-related. His turn is only getting funnier on Death Row (his pet name for the NHS) – can you spot him among the pestilence, the disease and the people who can't afford private healthcare? Urgh!

RECEPTION →

DOWN THE PUB

The history of politics is filled to brimming with boozers, but few can also claim to be bloody good blokes while they're at it. Especially Margaret Thatcher. Can you find the lesser-spotted Farage in his natural habitat? He's the only one wearing his UKIP rosette (which neatly doubles as a discount card at Poundland). And keep an eye out for pub landlord Al Murray, Nigel's mother and SamCam plus partner. Time, gentlemen, please!

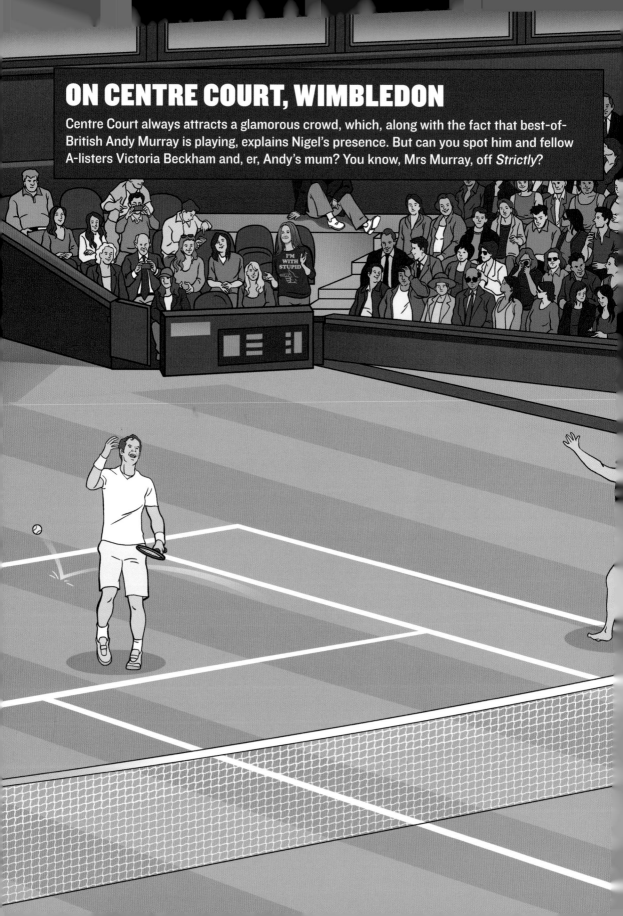

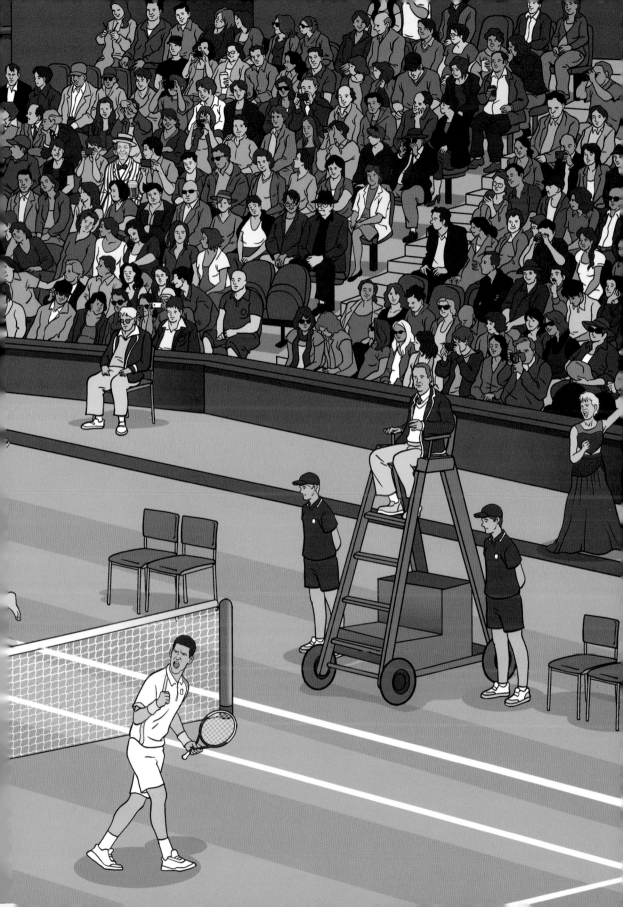

RIDING THE LONDON EYE

Lights, camera, action! Nigel's no stranger to the more glamorous side of politics – just ask his fashion disciples in the Countryside Alliance and Jeremy Clarkson – though it's advisable to keep selfie sticks out of his way. Barack Obama he is not. For a multitude of reasons.

AT NOTTING HILL CARNIVAL

Nothing screams diversity quite like the horde of drunken Antipodeans and middle-class white people who descend upon Notting Hill Carnival, a celebration led by the once-local (pre-gentrification) West Indian community. Nigel, naturally, is in his element – this is the reggae purist who got down to 'UKIP Calypso', remember – but can you spot Andrew 'plebgate' Mitchell doing what he does best?

AT A RESTAURANT

No one puts baby in the corner. Proud middle- and upper-class mothers unite against the tyranny of behind-closed-doors baby-feeding, but where's Nigel among this orgy of non-titillating breast and nipple?

AT LORD'S CRICKET GROUND

Nigel likes to compare the refined complexity of cricket to navigating the political devilry of the European Parliament, although at least with the latter there are no bloody Aussies to deal with. Can you spot legendary commentator David Lloyd? And what on earth are the Barmy Army saying to Shane Warne? Most Ukippers haven't heard that level of venom since their National Front days.

IN EUROPEAN PARLIAMENT, BRUSSELS

A man of sophistication and wit, Nigel embodies all the best bits from across the Channel (smoking) while remaining resolutely British. Can you find him in his home from home – a largely unnoticed political arena – as he communicates effortlessly with his continental cousins?

AT THE HUNT

When the two most charismatic men in British politics collide, something has to give. Unfortunately, that something is the humble pheasant, the prey in this most noble of pursuits and the meat in a Nigel and Boris Johnson sandwich. Can you find them both? Their ego one-upmanship should mean it won't take long.

AT TRAFALGAR SQUARE

Admiral of the fleet, the genius behind Britain's greatest naval victories and master of the deep-blue sea ... and this is how Lord Nelson is honoured: eternally alone on a column while tourists of all nations – yes, even the French and Spanish – pose for photos by the fountain below. Little wonder he's come out as a Ukipper. But where's the captain of the good ship UKIP among this mêlée?

THE ANSWERS

DOWNING STREET DREAM

AT HEATHROW

AT LEICESTER SQUARE

ON THE M4

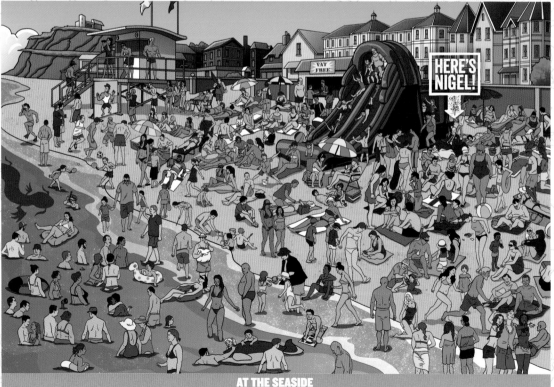

AT THE SEASIDE

IN HOSPITAL

DOWN THE PUB

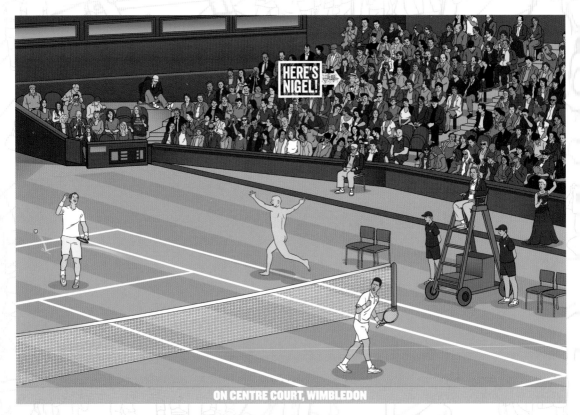

ON CENTRE COURT, WIMBLEDON

RIDING THE LONDON EYE

AT NOTTING HILL CARNIVAL

AT A RESTAURANT

AT LORD'S CRICKET GROUND

IN EUROPEAN PARLIAMENT, BRUSSELS

AT THE HUNT

AT TRAFALGAR SQUARE